First published in 2009 in Great Britain by
Barrington Stoke Ltd
18 Walker St, Edinburgh, EH3 7LP

www.barringtonstoke.co.uk

Title ISBN: 978-1-84299-651-5
Pack ISBN: 978-1-84299-725-3

Printed in Great Britain by the Charlesworth Group

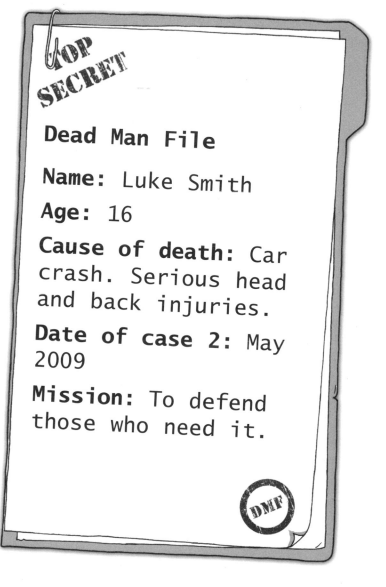

Dead Man File

Name: Luke Smith

Age: 16

Cause of death: Car crash. Serious head and back injuries.

Date of case 2: May 2009

Mission: To defend those who need it.

DMF

To Chris Garford and Ernie Matson

Contents

Name:
Luke Smith
Age:
16

Chapter 1

The ghosts of some people stay around the place where they died. After the crash that killed me, Luke, I spent a lot of time in the wood near Dead Man's Bend.

A tramp named Stan lived in that wood. I felt sorry for him. His wife had died and his children lived far away. He just left home one day and his family never saw him again.

Name:
Luke Smith
Age:
16

Chapter 2

All Stan's stuff was in his rucksack. He made a home in the wood among the trees and rocks.

He got water from the river and cooked his food on a camp fire.

He would go into the town and beg for money and food. He never got very much.

Name:
Luke Smith
Age:
16

Chapter 3

One night as Stan lay down to sleep, two men in a fast car came to see him.

"Let's have fun," said Ron. "I hate tramps."

"Put his bag on the fire," his mate Frank said. All Stan's stuff was in that bag.

Stan woke up. He was afraid. These
men could kill him. I had to help him.

Name:
Luke Smith
Age:
I6

Chapter 4

"What's that noise?" Frank asked.

"The car radio's come on," Ron said.

"Now I can hear the car horn," Frank
said.

"Someone has got into the car. But I
locked it." Ron looked at the key in his
hand.

"Let's go and see who it is," said Frank.

But Ron wasn't keen.

Name:
Luke Smith
Age:
I6

Chapter 5

Now for my best trick. I let the hand brake off and the car started to roll down the hill.

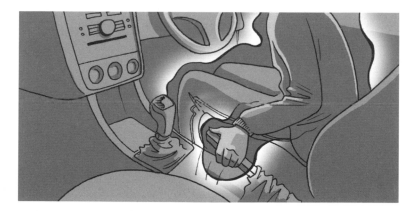

"The car's moving," Frank yelled.

Faster and faster the car went. Frank and Ron had no hope of stopping it.

At the bottom of the hill was the river and the car made a big splash, then went under the water.

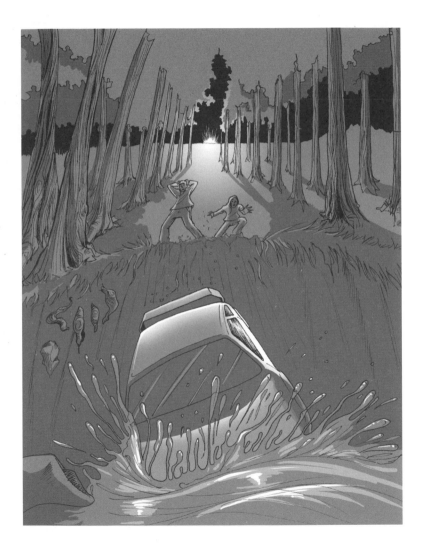

Chapter 6

"How did that happen?" Ron asked.

"Search me," Frank said.

They looked back up the hill and saw the light from Stan's fire.

"That tramp is evil," Ron said. "I'm never coming here again."

I felt good about saving Stan.

Like this book? Why not try the next one coming soon?

Spiker

Luke Smith is dead. But he's back to help those who need it.

Yasmin's drink is spiked. Can Luke warn her in time?

For more info check out our website:
www.barringtonstoke.co.uk

Also coming soon ...

Fire Escape

Luke Smith is dead. But he's back to help those who need it.

Dan is in danger. Can Luke help him?

For more info check out our website:
www.barringtonstoke.co.uk